Me and my Dad

A Little Book About

and my

Illustrated by Jedda Robaard

The Five Mile Press

The Five Mile Press Pty Ltd
1 Centre Road, Scoresby
Victoria 3179 Australia
www.fivemile.com.au

A Division of Bonnier Publishing Australia
www.bonnierpublishing.com

Copyright © The Five Mile Press Pty Ltd, 2013
Illustrations © Jedda Robaard

All rights reserved

First published 2013

Printed in China 5

This is a book to fill in and share with your dad.

You may need some help to complete it – that's what dads are for!

You can use the pouch in the back of the book to store photographs,

postcards, birthday cards, and anything else that is special to you and your dad.

Write a special message for your dad in the gift card provided.

This is my **dad** and **me**.

Draw or attach a photo of you and your dad here.

Dad was born
in a place called

Now he lives
in a place called

My dad's dad

is called

....

He is my grandpa!

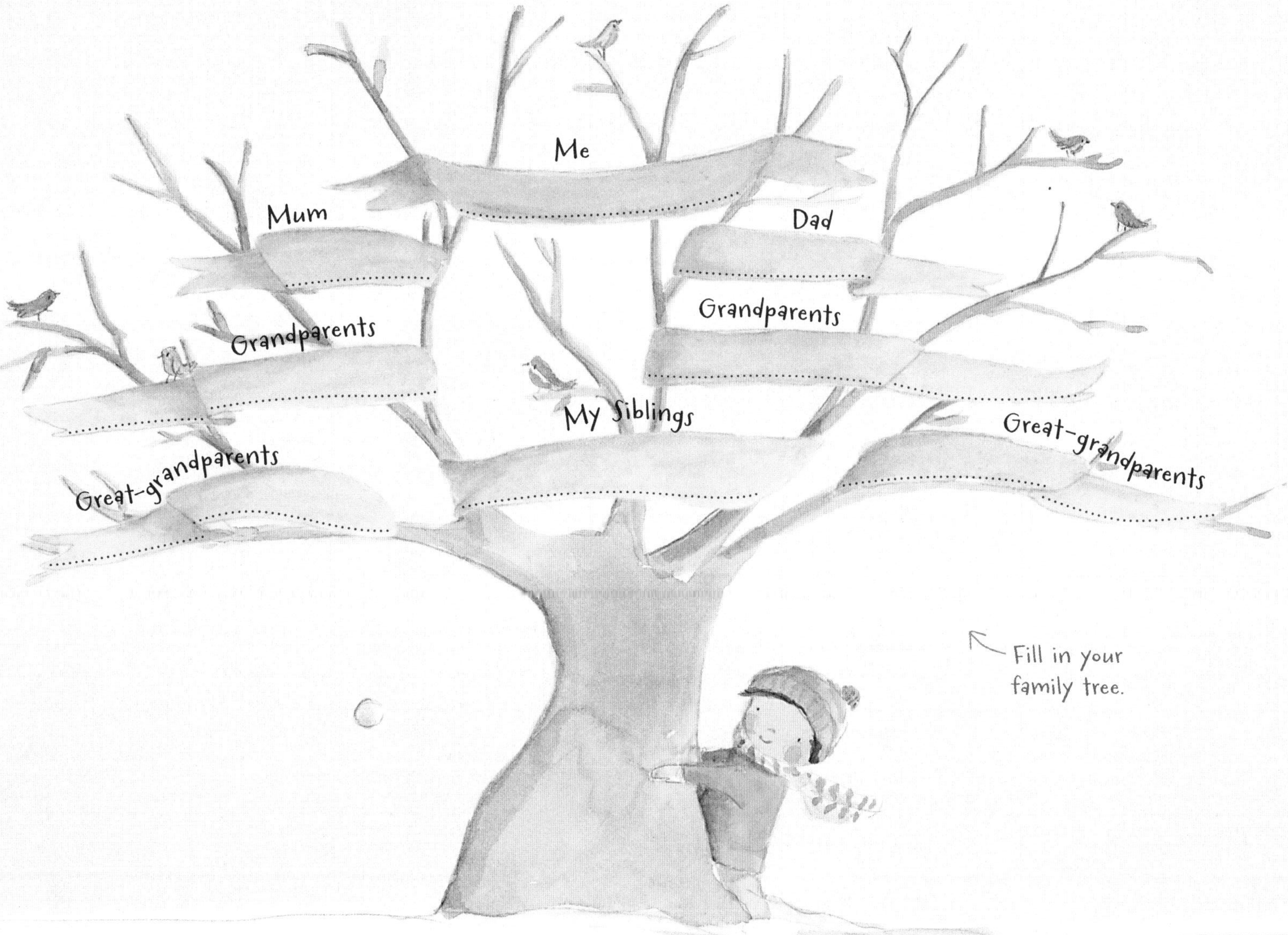

Me

Mum

Dad

Grandparents

Grandparents

My Siblings

Great-grandparents

Great-grandparents

My Family

Fill in your family tree.

When Dad was little,

his favourite sport was ....

Now his favourite sport is ....

My favourite sport is ....

.... Here is a picture of us playing together

Draw or attach a picture of you and your dad here.

When Dad
was young,

his favourite game was
. . . .

My favourite game is

....

Dad and I love playing
different games.

Our favourite games to
play together are:

....

....

....

Draw a picture of your
favourite game here.

When Dad was my age,

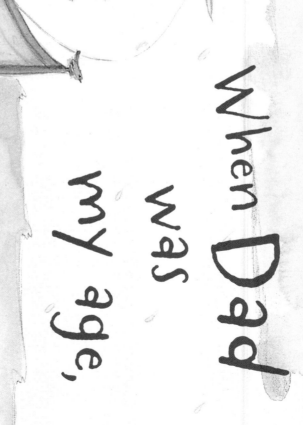

He looks happy / strong / funny / brave!

Here is a picture of my dad dressed as a ....

When I grow up, I want to be a ....

he wanted to be a ....

Draw a costume on Dad.

When
Dad
was
young,

his favourite music was

....
....
....
....

Now he likes to listen to

....
....
....
....

My favourite music is

....

Dad's
favourite
colour is

My favourite colour is
....

Colour in the birds.

Here are some birds in our favourite colours

Dad and I love to make things in the kitchen

Dad's best thing
to cook is

....

Our favourite thing
to eat is

....

Make a list or draw your favourite foods here.

My Dad
loves going on holidays.

His favourite holiday was

....

He has always wanted to go to

....

The best place Dad and I have been together is

....

Draw or attach a photo of you and your dad on holidays.

For my birthday,

Dad

likes to take me to the

....

The best thing we have done on my birthday is

....

My favourite birthday present from dad was

....

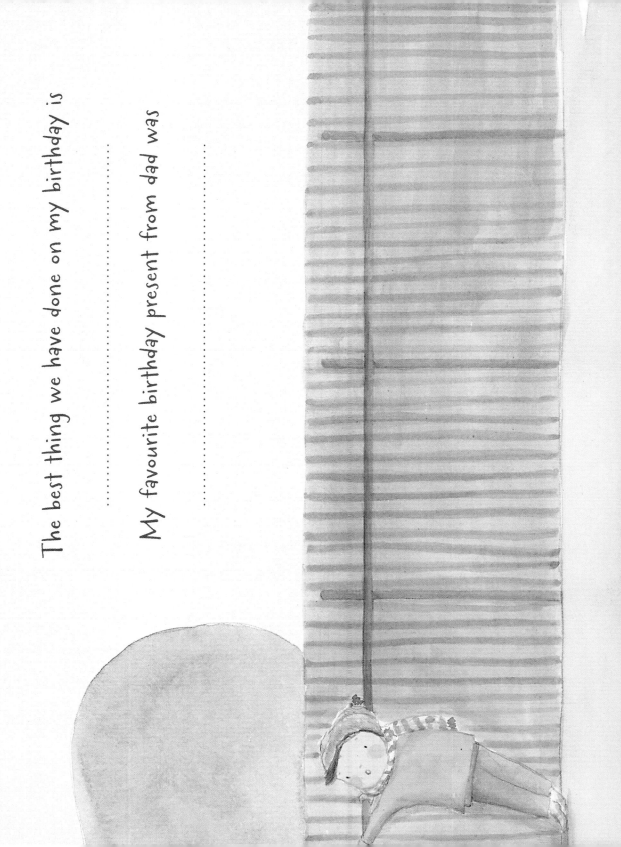

I love my dad

That's why I've made this special book and card just for him!